THE *BONE* SAGA

ROSE

BY JEFF SMITH

WITH ILLUSTRATIONS BY CHARLES VESS

An Imprint of
SCHOLASTIC

New York   Toronto   London   Auckland   Sydney   Mexico City   New Delhi   Hong Kong   Buenos Aires

This book is dedicated to Karen and Vijaya

Copyright © 2009 by Jeff Smith.

All rights reserved. Published by Graphix, an imprint of Scholastic Inc., *Publishers since 1920.* SCHOLASTIC, GRAPHIX, and associated logos are trademarks and/or registered trademarks of Scholastic Inc.

Library of Congress Catalog Card Number 9568403.
ISBN-13 978-0-545-13542-9 — ISBN-10 0-545-13542-7
ISBN 0-545-13543-5 (paperback)

ACKNOWLEDGMENTS
Harvestar Family Crest designed by Charles Vess
Map of *The Valley* by Mark Crilley
Illustration and font design by Charles Vess

10 9 8 7 6 5 4 3 2   09 10 11 12
First Scholastic edition, August 2009
Book design by David Saylor
Printed in Singapore 46

CONTENTS

When the world was very, very new, and dreams had not yet receded from the waking day...

The first dragon was a queen named Mim. And Mim was the keeper of all who dreamed.

She cared for the dreaming by encircling the world and holding her tail in her mouth...

As long as Mim held her tail in this way, balance was maintained.

And balance is most important, for the dreaming is a thing of great delicacy,

Without it, there could be no life.

MIM WATCHED THE DREAMING WITH CARE, AND ALL CREATURES LIVED TOGETHER IN PEACE AND HARMONY.

UNTIL ONE DAY A SPIRIT KNOWN AS THE LORD OF THE LOCUSTS BECAME UNHAPPY.

THE LORD OF THE LOCUSTS WAS A NIGHTMARE BEING WITHOUT SHAPE OR FORM WHO COULD EXIST ONLY IN THE SPIRIT WORLD.

HE WANTED TO MOVE ON THE FACE OF THIS WORLD, BUT TO DO THAT HE MUST TAKE POSSESSION OF A MORTAL BEING'S FLESH.

HE CHOSE MIM, QUEEN OF THE DRAGONS. THE MOST POWERFUL DREAMER OF ALL.

THE LORD OF THE LOCUSTS ENTERED HER MIND AND THE QUEEN OF THE DRAGONS WENT MAD.

BALANCE WAS LOST AND THE WORLD WENT DARK.

THE DREAM BECAME A NIGHTMARE.

TO SAVE THE WORLD, THE OTHER DRAGONS WERE FORCED TO MOVE AGAINST HER.

A TERRIBLE BATTLE ENSUED.

AS THE DRAGONS FOUGHT WITH THEIR MAD QUEEN, THEY CRASHED BACK AND FORTH, PUSHING UP ROCKS AND MOUNTAINS.

ON AND ON THE BATTLE WAGED, WITH MANY VALIANT DRAGONS LOSING THEIR LIVES.

UNTIL AT LAST THE DRAGONS KNEW THEY MUST TAKE DESPERATE MEASURES.

THEY KNEW IT WOULD BE THE END OF THEIR BELOVED MIM...

BUT FOR THE GOOD OF THE WORLD AND TO DESTROY THEIR ENEMY...

...THEY TURNED THEIR QUEEN INTO STONE--

--TRAPPING THE LORD OF LOCUSTS INSIDE HER FOREVER.

LATER, THE LAND COOLED...

AND THAT IS HOW THE VALLEY WAS BORN--

ROSE! ARE YOU PAYING ATTENTION?

WHAT?

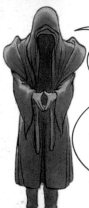

YOU WERE LETTING YOUR MIND WANDER AGAIN, ROSE.

YOU MUST LEARN TO FOCUS. THIS IS NOT JUST A HISTORY LESSON...THIS IS AN EXERCISE TO BUILD AWARENESS IN YOUR DREAMS.

WHY ARE YOU ALWAYS PICKING ON ME?

WHY DON'T YOU PICK ON BRIAR FOR A CHANGE?

BRIAR DOES NOT HAVE THE GIFT THAT YOU HAVE.

HER DREAMING EYE IS BLIND, YOU KNOW THAT.

I...I'M SORRY, BRIAR. YOU KNOW I DIDN'T MEAN THAT.

IT'S ALL RIGHT.

REALLY?! WE'RE GOING TO OLD MAN'S CAVE TOMORROW? BRIAR—— DID YOU HEAR THAT?

AREN'T YOU EXCITED? WE ARE GOING TO TAKE A JOURNEY TO THE NORTHERN END OF THE VALLEY! IT'S SO BEAUTIFUL THIS TIME OF YEAR.

WHY ARE WE GOING?

WE AREN'T SUPPOSED TO TAKE OUR FINAL TEST UNTIL WE ARE OLDER.

THE HEADMASTER FEELS YOU TWO ARE READY. THE CAPTAIN OF THE GUARD WILL ACCOMPANY YOU AT DAWN.

WILL YOU NOT RESPECT OUR WISHES, BRIAR? WE BELIEVE THERE IS STILL HOPE FOR YOU.

THERE IS NO HOPE. TAKING THE TEST IS A WASTE OF TIME.

BRIAR, HOW CAN YOU SAY SUCH A THING? I'M SURE YOUR DREAMING EYE WILL OPEN———

DO NOT PATRONIZE ME, MY SISTER.

IF I MUST, I WILL BE READY TO LEAVE AT DAWN.

IT'S A BAD ONE--- I--- THINK I'D BETTER GO TELL THE CAPTAIN OF THE GUARD.

YES, BY ALL MEANS. I DON'T KNOW HOW THE REST OF US WOULD EVER MANAGE WITHOUT THE HELP OF YOUR SPECIAL DREAMING TALENTS.

CAPTAIN DOWN!

YES, PRINCESS?

CAPTAIN, I HAVE THAT GITCHY FEELING AGAIN--

AND IT'S WORSE THAN BEFORE! I FEAR THERE MAY BE DANGER NEARBY.

HMM. YOUR DOGS DON'T SEEM TO SENSE ANYTHING OUT OF THE ORDINARY.

THE GITCHY FEELING OFTEN WARNS ME OF DANGER LONG BEFORE EUCLID OR CLEO SENSE ANYTHING---

ALL RIGHT, PRINCESS.

I WILL SPEAK WITH THE VENI-YAN GUARDS. STAY CLOSE TO YOUR SISTER.

YES, OF COURSE.

THE PRINCESS ROSE IS WARNING US OF DANGER NEARBY. DO EITHER OF YOU SENSE ANYTHING?

I SENSE NOTHING UNUSUAL.

NOR DO I, BUT PRINCESS ROSE IS KNOWN FOR HER SKILLS IN PRESCIENCE.

BANDITS?

POSSIBLY. WE SHOULD BE WATCHFUL.

THERE IS ANOTHER DANGER... THE HAIRY MEN.

HAIRY MEN? YOU MEAN THE RAT CREATURES? WHAT WOULD THEY BE DOING THIS FAR NORTH?

THERE ARE REPORTS OF INDIVIDUALS MIGRATING NORTH ALONG THE EASTERN MOUNTAINS.

WHY DIDN'T YOU TELL ME EARLIER?

IT WAS CONSIDERED A MATTER FOR THE VENI-YAN ORDER. THE HEADMASTER AT OLD MAN'S CAVE IS TRACKING THE SITUATION.

THE HAIRY MEN MAY BE RESPONDING TO A MINOR FLUCTUATION IN THE EARTH'S HUM. IT SHOULD NOT AFFECT US, OR OUR PROGRESS.

UNLESS ONE OF THEM ATTACKS US.

IF THERE'S ANYTHING ELSE THE "ORDER" KNOWS THAT MIGHT AFFECT THE SAFETY OF OUR PRINCESSES, I EXPECT TO BE INFORMED IMMEDIATELY. UNDERSTAND?

YES, CAPTAIN.

LIFE IS FLEETING... THE WORLD IS JUST A DREAM.

IT IS SAID THAT A HUMAN LIFE IS MUCH LIKE A SPARROW FLYING FROM WINTER DARKNESS INTO A LIGHTED HALL-- INTO THE WARMTH FOR A MOMENT--

--THEN OUT ONCE MORE INTO THE NIGHT.

WITH YOUR DREAMING EYE YOU MUST LEARN TO SEE BEYOND THE LIGHTED HALL OF YOUR BEING...

...OUT INTO THE LARGER, COLDER, MOONLIT WORLD OF THE DREAMING.

ONCE YOU CAN SEE ALL THINGS AT ONCE, YOU WILL BECOME ONE WITH CREATION.

IMPOSSIBLE!

YOU HAVE A QUESTION, PRINCESS BRIAR?

I HAVE DIFFICULTY BELIEVING THAT ANYONE CAN SEE EVERYTHING ALL AT ONE TIME.

IT IS A MATTER OF PERSPECTIVE.

PRETEND THE LINE THAT I AM TRACING IN THE SAND IS A MIGHTY RIVER.

When you stand on the shore, all you see is the riverbank...

But from the height of a sparrow, you can see the course of the entire river.

Enough, Headmaster! I demand to know why we were brought to this wilderness in the midst of winter?

Briar! We were brought here for our final tests. We may be princesses, but we must speak with respect to the Headmaster!

He is hiding something from us, my sister. Apparently your dreaming eye cannot save you from your own naivete.

Is this true, Headmaster? Are you hiding something?

It is true. There is something more to tell you...

The reason for the secrecy was for your safety. Please forgive me.

DREAMS AND OMENS DO NOT RULE MY DESTINY, ROSE!

BRIAR, PLEASE! IT IS A BREACH OF THE HIGHEST PROTOCOL TO REMOVE YOUR HOOD INSIDE OLD MAN'S CAVE!

YOU MAY ALLOW YOURSELF TO BE MANIPULATED, BUT I WILL NOT!

LOOK OUT!

WELL, HELLO, LITTLE ONE. WHAT DO YOU WANT?

JUST TO WARM YOURSELF BY OUR FIRE FOR A MOMENT?

WHAT KEY? WHAT ARE WE LOOKING FOR?

AN OBJECT TO FOCUS ON-- WE'LL KNOW IT WHEN WE SEE IT--

---THERE IT IS! A SPARROW!

A SPARROW? WHY?

I WAS JUST TALKING TO THE HEADMASTER ABOUT A SPARROW!

NOW IF I FOCUS ON THE BIRD, SHE AND EVERYTHING AROUND HER WILL BECOME MORE SOLID AND I WILL BE ABLE TO CONTROL THE DREAM! IT'S WHAT I'M LEARNING IN MEDITATION.

WHY DO YOU WANT TO CONTROL YOUR DREAMS?

THAT'S WHAT I KEEP ASKING, BUT MY TEACHERS---

WELL, OKAY THEN, LET'S FOCUS ON THAT BIRD!

I'M BEGINNING TO WONDER IF THE ICE QUEEN ISN'T RIGHT. WHY DID YOUR MOTHER AND FATHER SEND US ON THIS CRAZY ADVENTURE IN THE FIRST PLACE?

YES, BUT COULDN'T WE HAVE DONE IT IN ATHEIA INSTEAD OF THIS BACKWARD PLACE?

OLD MAN'S CAVE IS THE SANCTUARY OF THE DISCIPLES OF VENU. THIS IS WHERE I MUST PASS MY FINAL TEST!

BECAUSE AS A MEMBER OF THE ROYAL FAMILY, I MUST BE TRAINED TO LEAD THE DISCIPLES OF VENU AS WELL AS OUR PEOPLE.

HOLD IT! DID YOU SEE THAT?

LOOK AT THAT PERSON GOING INTO THE MOUNTAINS!

THAT LOOKS LIKE BRIAR! ISN'T SHE SUPPOSED TO BE IN YOUR CLASS WITH YOU?

I WONDER WHAT SHE'S UP TO?

SHE'S DEFINITELY NOT GOING TO CLASS. COME ON! LET'S FOLLOW HER!

ARE YOU SURE THAT'S A GOOD IDEA?

WOOF!
WOOF!
AAH!
WOOF!
IT'S-- IT'S JUST A SWARM OF GRASSHOPPERS!
IT LOOKED JUST LIKE A GIANT VERSION OF YOU!
IT MUST HAVE BEEN A TRICK OF THE LIGHT!
THE DRAGON WAS RIGHT! SHE REALLY IS HER OWN WORST ENEMY!
THAT'S NOT WHAT HE MEANT AND YOU KNOW IT!
NOW, COME, DOGS! WE'RE GOING ON!
I THINK THAT'S WHAT HE MEANT!

YOU KNOW, SOMETHING ABOUT THIS PLACE IS FAMILIAR...

I KNOW! THIS IS THE SAME MOUNTAINSIDE FROM MY DREAM!

JUST OVER THIS RIDGE IS A SMALL STREAM FLOWING OVER GRASS.

AND IN THE STREAM WAS A POOR, HELPLESS LITTLE DRAGON.

WHAT'S THAT ROARING SOUND?

THIS IS YOUR IDEA OF A SMALL STREAM?

IN MY DREAM, IT WAS MUCH SMALLER.

PRINCESS ROSE. . .

WHO SAID THAT?

I DID. . .

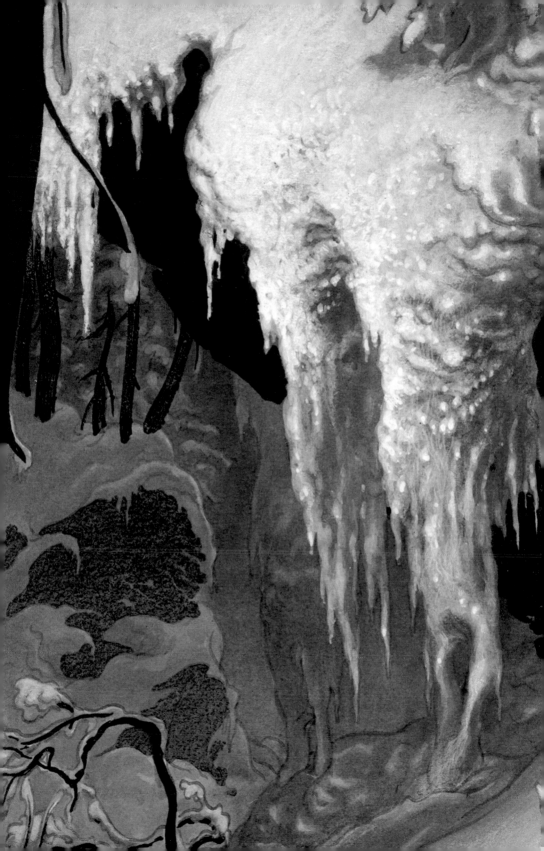

THE CAVE

WE HAVE RECEIVED VERY BAD TIDINGS TODAY.

A MEMBER OF THE RACE OF DRAGONS HAS GONE MAD.

HAVE YOU SEEN HIM?

I -- I HAVE SEEN A DRAGON . . .

GO ON.

HE SPOKE TO ME OF HAVING A NEW MASTER.

A NEW MASTER?

MY HEART IS SUDDENLY HEAVY, YOUR MAJESTY.

AS YOU KNOW, THE EMANCIPATOR OF THE LOCUST IS FORETOLD.

THE DRAGONS HAVE LONG KNOWN THAT THE EMANCIPATOR WILL BE A CREATURE WITH A VERY POWERFUL DREAMING EYE.

POWERFUL ENOUGH TO ENSLAVE EVEN A DRAGON.

COULD BALSAAD'S NEW MASTER BE THIS EMANCIPATOR?

WAIT.

COME IN MY ROOM. LET'S TALK.

IF YOU WISH.

ROSE, WHEN OUR PARENTS FIRST SENT US HERE FOR OUR TESTS, I WAS PREPARED FOR THE COUNCIL TO CHOOSE YOU AS THE CROWN PRINCESS.

Click

ME?

DON'T BE SILLY. YOU'RE OLDER AND SMARTER THAN ME, BRIAR. YOU KNOW THE COUNCIL WILL CHOOSE YOU TO BE OUR NEXT QUEEN.

WE BOTH KNOW THAT I CAN'T PASS THE TEST.

YOUR DREAMING EYE WILL OPEN SOON!

EVEN IF MY EYE WERE OPEN, ROSE, YOU KNOW I'M NOT POPULAR. NOT LIKE YOU.

THE COUNCIL WILL CHOOSE YOU.

OH, BRIAR.

THAT'S WHY I FIND IT SO STRANGE THAT THE GREAT RED DRAGON ACCUSED YOU OF BEING THE EMANCIPATOR.

ROSE HAS RUN OFF TO FIGHT THE ROGUE DRAGON BY HERSELF.

WHAT?!

SHE CAN'T FIGHT THAT MONSTER ON HER OWN!

DON'T WORRY, PRINCESS! MY MEN WILL FIND YOUR SISTER.

NO, LUCIUS, WAIT--

DELAY YOUR MEN UNTIL MIDNIGHT.

WHAT DO YOU MEAN?

ROSE IS CONFUSED-- FRIGHTENED. THE MEETING WITH THE HEADMASTER EMBARRASSED HER.

LET ME GO ALONE. I'LL BRING HER BACK BEFORE ANYONE KNOWS SHE IS GONE.

PLEASE?

WHAT YOU ARE ASKING ME TO DO, BRIAR-- I CAN'T--

PLEASE, MY LOVE, THIS IS IMPORTANT TO ME.

IF I CAN'T FIND ROSE, I WILL MEET YOU AND YOUR MEN AT THE STONE BRIDGE IN CONKLE'S HOLLOW.

VERY WELL. THE STROKE OF MIDNIGHT.

CRUNCH

SHH! IT'S VERY RARE TO SEE ONE OF THE HAIRY MEN THESE DAYS.

THEY ARE GENTLE CREATURES IF LEFT ALONE.

CRNCH

CRUNCH CRINCH

OF COURSE, I DID LET ONE RIDER GO TO OLD MAN'S CAVE FOR HELP...

BUT EVERYONE ELSE STAYS!

NOW, I'M GOING TO HAVE TO TRUST YOU FOR A LITTLE WHILE BECAUSE THE MASTER CALLS.

BUT I PROMISE I WON'T BE LONG!

DON'T TRY TO ESCAPE, OR I'LL FIND YOU IN THE WOODS AND FRY YOUR BONES!

GAK! GAK!

WHY IS THE MONSTER TOYING WITH US?

I DON'T KNOW. WE CAN ONLY HOPE THAT HELP ARRIVES SOON.

LET'S GET THESE CHILDREN INSIDE BEFORE IT COMES BACK.

THE PEOPLE OF OAK BOTTOM CAN'T WAIT FOR COUNCILS!

THEY NEED HELP NOW!

DEALING WITH A ROGUE DRAGON IS DANGEROUS AND DELICATE WORK, EVEN FOR OTHER DRAGONS.

LET ALONE UNTESTED PRINCESSES.

THERE MUST BE SOME OTHER REASON YOU FEEL THE NEED TO RUSH OFF AND FIGHT BALSAAD BY YOURSELF.

WELL?

MISTRESS? IS THE DRAGON UPSETTING YOU?

DO YOU WANT US TO CHASE HIM AWAY?

NO, EUCLID. NO, CLEO.

THE DRAGON IS RIGHT. I HAVE A CONFESSION TO MAKE.

I LIED TO THE HEADMASTER. I AM RESPONSIBLE FOR FREEING BALSAAD.

THE RIVER DRAGON APPEARED TO ME IN A DREAM ASKING FOR HELP.

BUT HE SEEMED SO HARMLESS! AND I ONLY LIED BECAUSE IT WAS JUST A DREAM, AND I DIDN'T WANT BRIAR TO GET IN TROUBLE--

JUST A DREAM?

HOW CAN YOU SAY THAT?

YOU ARE A DREAM MASTER IN TRAINING, A DISCIPLE OF VENU.

YOU KNOW THAT DREAMS CONTAIN TREMENDOUS POWER AND DEPTH... UNEXPLORED REACHES THAT PLUNGE DOWN TO YOUR VERY CORE...

AND THERE--AT THAT SMALLEST AND DEEPEST OF TOUCH POINTS--YOU ARE OPEN TO ALL THE POWER SOURCES OF THE UNIVERSE.

SINCE YOU DRAW ON THESE ENERGIES FOR YOUR OWN GITCHY FEELING, YOU KNOW SUCH MATTERS ARE NOT TO BE TAKEN LIGHTLY.

GET DOWN, YOU FOOLS!

WHO ARE YOU?

STAY DOWN-- WHILE I TAKE A LOOK.

HOLD IT, MISSY-- THERE'S A MAD DRAGON UP THERE!

QUIET!

WHO'S SHE TELLIN' TO BE QUIET?

WAIT, TOBY! DON'T YOU RECOGNIZE HER? IT'S PRINCESS ROSE!

I DON'T CARE IF SHE'S QUEEN VEN HERSELF-- SHE'S GONNA GET US KILLED!

IT'S BALSAAD! BUT HE DOESN'T SEE US!

YOU'RE NOT BRIAR! WHO ARE YOU?

YOUR SISTER HAS GIVEN HER LIFE TO ME.

YOU'RE MIM! THE FIRST QUEEN OF THE DRAGONS!

NO. MIM ALSO GAVE HER LIFE TO ME. I HAVE ALL HER POWER AND BRIAR'S.

BUT MIM TRICKED ME.

MIM SAVED THE WORLD BY GOING MAD AND FORCING HER OWN KIND TO TRAP ME IN STONE!

SO I NEED MORE STRENGTH TO FREE ME.

I NEED THE EMANCIPATOR.

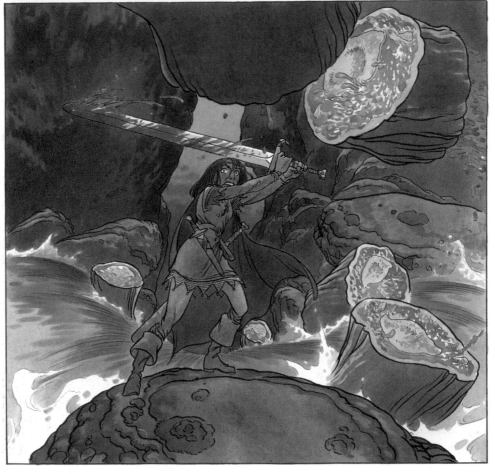

SNIK

HE TURNED ME INTO AN OLD CRONE TO PUNISH ME FOR MY FAILURE.

HELP ME, ROSE. I--

ROSE? WHY ARE YOU HOLDING THAT KNIFE?

I GAVE MY WORD TO THE GREAT RED DRAGON THAT I WOULD KILL THE FIRST LIVING CREATURE I SAW . . .

OH, HAVE MERCY, MY SISTER!

I DIDN'T KNOW WHAT I WAS DOING-- THE LOCUST CONTROLLED ME--

PLEASE HAVE MERCY.

WHAT CAN I DO? I GAVE MY WORD TO THE RED DRAGON.

KILL THE DOG INSTEAD. YOU SAW IT AT ALMOST THE SAME TIME-- THE DRAGON WON'T CARE IF YOU SUBSTITUTE AS LONG AS BALANCE IS MAINTAINED.

PLEASE, SISTER.

I'M YOUR OWN *FLESH AND BLOOD.*

I BEG YOU TO DO THE *RIGHT* THING.

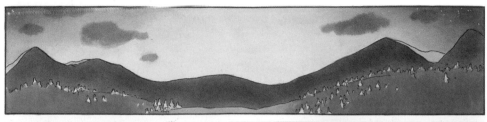

ROSE!

WHERE ARE YOU?

SPREAD OUT ALONG THE RIVER!

HERE I AM!

PRINCESS!

THANK GOODNESS YOU'RE OKAY!

BALSAAD IS DEAD. WASHED DOWN THE RIVER IN A HUNDRED PIECES.

BRIAR NEEDS HELP.

CLEO?

THIS IS BRIAR?

THE LOCUST DID THIS TO HER.

BE GENTLE. SHE'S SUFFERED A LOT.

I'M AFRAID WE ALL HAVE MUCH SUFFERING TO DO.

MISTRESS?

WHERE'S CLEO?

OH, EUCLID.

IS SHE COMING?

NO. SHE'S NOT.

WHY NOT?

BECAUSE SHE HAD TO GIVE HER LIFE TO SPARE BRIAR'S LIFE.

OH, EUCLID, WHAT HAVE I DONE?

I MISS HER.

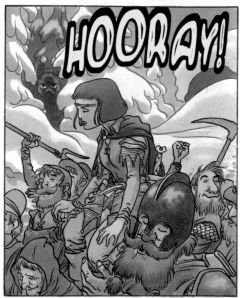

THE END

About JEFF SMITH

JEFF SMITH was born and raised in the American Midwest and learned about cartooning from comic strips, comic books, and watching animated shorts on TV. After four years of drawing comic strips for The Ohio State University's student newspaper and co-founding Character Builders animation studio in 1986, Smith launched the comic book *BONE* in 1991. Between *BONE* and other comics projects, Smith spends much of his time on the international guest circuit promoting comics and the art of graphic novels. Visit him at www.boneville.com.

About CHARLES VESS

CHARLES VESS has published award-winning works with Marvel, DC, and Cartoon Books, and one of his two Eisner awards was for his paintings in *Rose*. Vess collaborated with Neil Gaiman on their book *Stardust* (now a movie on DVD), for which he won the World Fantasy Award for Best Artist in 1999. He also illustrated *Seven Wild Sisters*, written by Charles de Lint, and *The Green Man: Tales from the Mythic Forest*, both of which were American Library Association Best Books. The design and co-sculpting of a bronze fountain based on *A Midsummer Night's Dream* has kept him busy for the last two years. Vess lives on a small farm in Virginia, and you can visit him at www.greenmanpress.com.

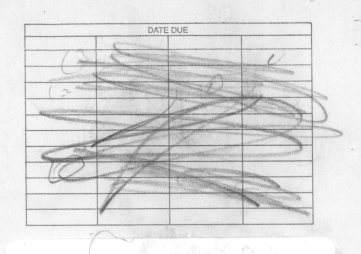

DATE DUE